# TALK OF THE BLOCK
## Short-Vowel Stories and Activities
### Health

**Ann Haffner**
ESL/Literacy Educator

D1295029

**New Readers Press**

*I gratefully acknowledge the support of the Massachusetts Department of Education/Young Adults with Learning Disabilities (YALD) Project, and the efforts of Bob Bickerton, Sheila Petruccelli, Ashley Hager, and Betty Stone.*

*I would also like to thank the teachers and students who reviewed the materials and gave valuable feedback. Thanks in particular to JoAnne Hartel, Betsy Lowry, Sylvia Greene, and Mary Lugton for their important contributions. I want to acknowledge the contribution of Billy Haffner to the original Talk of the Block books. I especially thank John Lugton for his support and love.*

*Finally, I wish to thank my students, whose determination to learn has been my ultimate inspiration.*

—**Ann Haffner**

Funded by
Massachusetts Department of Education
Young Adults with Learning Disabilities Project

Talk of the Block: Short-Vowel Stories and Activities
Health
ISBN 1-56420-420-0

**Acquisitions Editor:** Paula L. Schlusberg
**Content Editor:** Terrie Lipke
**Production Manager:** Andrea Woodbury
**Designer:** Andrea Woodbury
**Illustrations:** Carolyn Boehmer, Linda Tiff, James Wallace
**Production Specialist:** Jeffrey R. Smith
**Cover Design:** Kimbrly Koennecke

# CONTENTS

■

# TO THE STUDENT

This book is written for you.
It tells the stories of real people.
The stories are about health.

We hope you enjoy the stories.
We hope they will help you tell
your story too.

Good luck!
Happy reading!

# WELCOME
# TO HILL STREET

1  Welcome.

2  This is Hill Street.

3  This is a block on Hill Street.

4  Hill Street has a lot of shops.

5  Hill Street has a clinic.

6  Welcome to Hill Street.

7 This is Pam.

8 Pam lives on Hill Street.

9 This is Jack.

10 Jack lives on Hill Street.

11 This is Kim.

12 Kim has two kids.

13 Kim lives on Hill Street with the kids.

14 This is Bob.

15 Bob has a job on Hill Street.

16 Welcome to Hill Street.

**Circle *yes* or *no*.**

1. This is Hill Street.                 (yes)        no

2. Hill Street has a lot of shops.      yes          no

3. Pam lives on Hill Road.              yes          no

4. Jack lives on Hill Street.           yes          no

5. Kim lives on Hill Street.            yes          no

6. Kim has three kids.                  yes          no

7. Kim lives with the kids.             yes          no

8. Pam has two kids.                    yes          no

9. Jack has a job on Hill Street.       yes          no

10. Bob has a clinic on Hill Street.    yes          no

**Write the word.**

| word choices | sentence |
|---|---|
| Hill   Hall | **1.** This is _____Hill_____ Street. |
| shops   shoes | **2.** Hill Street has a lot of _____. |
| his   has | **3.** Hill Street _____ a clinic. |
| gives   lives | **4.** Pam _____ on Hill Street. |
| is   its | **5.** This _____ Jack. |
| kinds   kids | **6.** Kim has two _____. |
| with   what | **7.** Kim lives _____ the kids. |
| Stop   Street | **8.** Kim lives on Hill _____. |
| Bob   Bill | **9.** _____ has a job on Hill Street. |
| it   to | **10.** Welcome _____ Hill Street. |

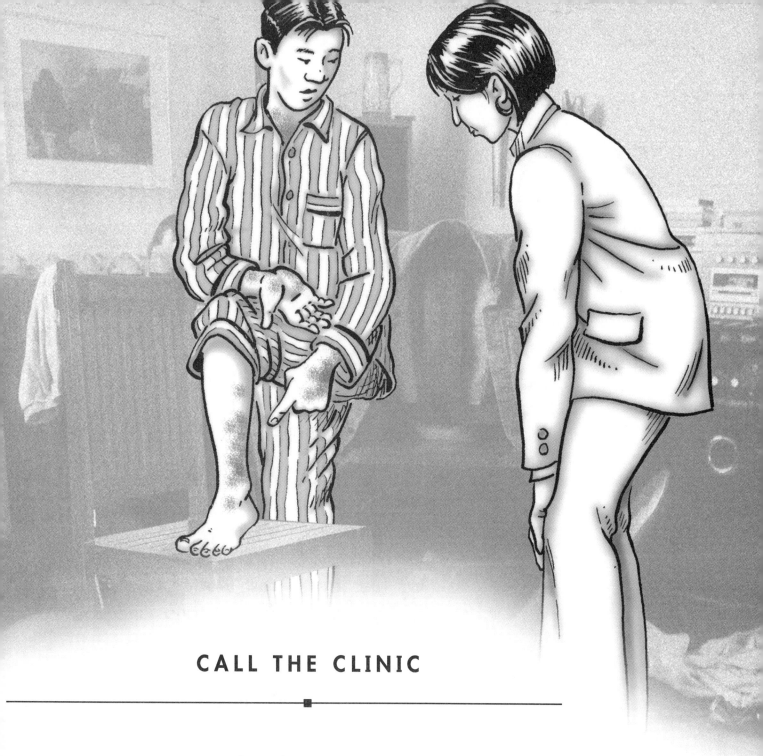

## CALL THE CLINIC

---

1  It is Wednesday.
2  Kim's son is sick.
3  Ben has a rash.
4  It is a bad rash.

5  Kim calls Hill Street Clinic.
6  Her son has to see the doctor.

7 Hello. This is Pam at Hill Street Clinic.
8 May I help you?

9 Yes. This is Kim Lee.
10 My son, Ben, is sick.

11 What's the matter?

12 He has a bad rash.
13 On Monday, the rash was on his chest.
14 On Tuesday, the rash was on his neck.
15 Today, the rash is on his hands and legs.

16 Can you bring him in today at 1:00 p.m.?

17 Yes, I can.
18 Thank you.

**Write the answer.**

1. What day is it?

   <u>It is Wednesday.</u>

2. What does Kim's son have?

   _____

3. What does Kim call?

   _____

4. Who does her son have to see?

   _____

5. Where is the rash today?

   _____

6. What time can Kim bring her son to the clinic?

   _____

**Write the word.**

| | | | |
|---|---|---|---|
| doctor | Monday | rash | Tuesday |
| hands | Pam | son | Wednesday |

1. Kim calls Hill Street Clinic on ___Wednesday___ .

2. Her son has a bad _____ .

3. He has to see the _____ .

4. Kim talks to _____ on the phone.

5. On _____ , the rash was on his chest.

6. On _____ , the rash was on his neck.

7. Today, the rash is on his _____ and legs.

8. Kim will bring her _____ to the clinic today.

## Write the word.

1.  It _____*is*_____ Wednesday.

2.  Kim's son _____ sick.

3.  He _____ a bad rash.

4.  He _____ a rash on his chest and neck.

5.  Today, the rash _____ on his hands and legs.

6.  Pam _____ at Hill Street Clinic.

## BOB IS SICK

1  This is Bob.
2  Bob is in bed.
3  Bob is sick in bed.

4  Bob can't go to work.
5  He calls the boss.

6 "I am sick," says Bob.
7 "I can't come to work today."

8 "OK, Bob," says the boss.
9 "I want you to get well.
10 You can get help.
11 You can get help at the clinic."

12 "Thank you," says Bob.
13 "I will call the clinic.
14 I will go to the clinic today."

**Circle *yes* or *no*.**

1. Bob is in bed.            yes       no

2. Bob is sick.            yes       no

3. Bob can go to work.            yes       no

4. Bob calls the boss.            yes       no

5. The boss is sick.            yes       no

6. Bob will get help.            yes       no

7. Bob will call his mother.            yes       no

8. Bob will go to school.            yes       no

9. Bob will go to the clinic.            yes       no

10. He will go to the clinic Wednesday.       yes       no

**Write the word.**

| | |
|---|---|
| bad   bed | **1.** Bob is sick in _____. |
| walk   work | **2.** Bob can't go to _____. |
| boss   bills | **3.** Bob calls his _____. |
| sit   sick | **4.** "I am _____," says Bob. |
| well   will | **5.** The boss wants Bob to get _____. |
| go   get | **6.** Bob can _____ help. |
| block   clinic | **7.** He can get help at the _____. |
| thanks   thinks | **8.** Bob _____ his boss. |
| call   ill | **9.** Bob will _____ the clinic. |
| Tuesday   today | **10.** He will go to the clinic _____. |

**Write the word.**

| at | in | to |
|---|---|---|

This is Bob.

**1.** Bob is _____ bed.

**2.** Bob is sick _____ bed.

**3.** Bob is not _____ work.

Bob calls the boss.

**4.** He can't go _____ work today.

**5.** The boss wants Bob _____ get well.

Bob can get help.

**6.** The boss wants Bob _____ get help.

**7.** He can get help _____ the clinic.

**8.** Bob will go _____ the clinic today.

## AT THE CLINIC

1   Bob is at Hill Street Clinic.

2   Bob is sick.

3   He wants to get well.

4   Pam works at Hill Street Clinic.

5   She sits at a big desk.

6 Bob tells Pam,

7 "I have an appointment.

8 I have an appointment with the doctor."

9 Pam helps Bob with his appointment.

10 Pam asks, "What is your first name?

11 What is your last name?"

12 Bob tells her, "My name is Bob Finn."

13 Pam asks Bob to spell his last name.

14 "F-I-N-N," Bob says.

15 Pam tells Bob to sit.

16 Bob sits and sits and sits.

17 Bob sits and thinks, "I am sick of this clinic."

18 Then Pam stands up. She says,

19 "Bob Finn. The doctor can see you."

**Write the answer.**

1. Where is Bob?

   _____

2. Who works at Hill Street Clinic?

   _____

3. What does Bob tell Pam?

   _____

4. How does Bob spell his last name?

   _____

5. What does Pam tell Bob to do?

   _____

6. Who can see Bob?

   _____

**Write the word.**

| appointment | doctor | spell | well |
| big | sits | tells | works |

**1.** Bob wants to get _____.

**2.** Pam _____ at Hill Street Clinic.

**3.** She sits at a _____ desk.

**4.** Bob has an _____ with the doctor.

**5.** Pam asks Bob to _____ his last name.

**6.** Pam _____ Bob to sit.

**7.** Bob _____ and thinks.

**8.** Pam says, "The _____ can see you."

**Circle.**

---

# HILL STREET CLINIC

28 Hill Street • 555-7328

You have an appointment on:

__Tuesday__        __04/19/05__

      Day                 Date

At __1:15__        a.m.    p.m.

---

**1.** The appointment is on First Street.     yes     no

**2.** The appointment is at a clinic.     yes     no

**3.** The appointment is on Thursday.     yes     no

**4.** The appointment is on Tuesday.     yes     no

**5.** The appointment is at 11:15.     yes     no

**6.** The appointment is in the morning.     yes     no

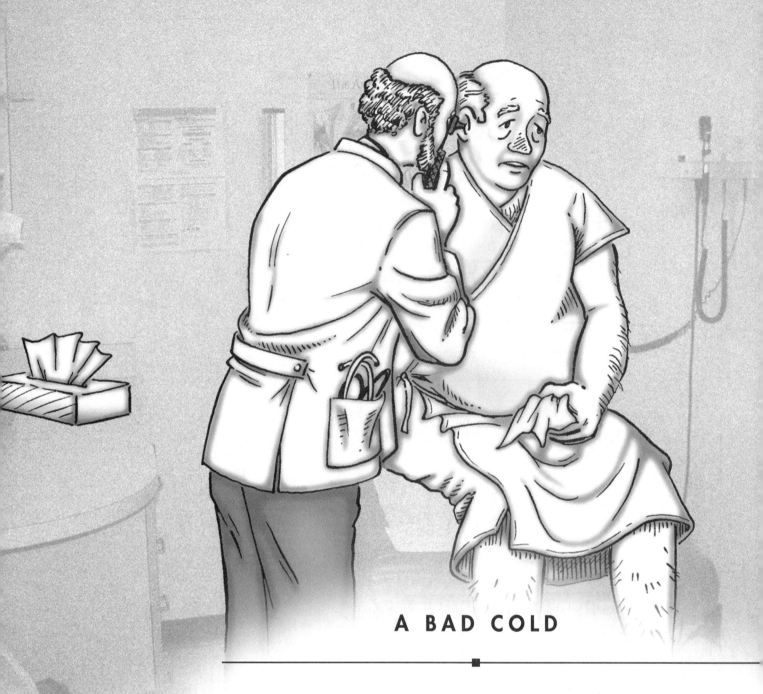

## A BAD COLD

■

1 Bob is with the doctor.
2 He is with the doctor at Hill Street Clinic.
3 Bob says, "I don't feel well. I feel ill."

4 The doctor tells Bob,
5 "You have a bad cold.

7  The doctor says, "Don't go to work.
8  Get a lot of rest.
9  Drink a lot of water."

10  Bob asks the doctor,
11  "Will you give me pills?
12  Will pills fix my cold?"

13  The doctor tells Bob,
14  "Pills can help some things.
15  But pills can't fix a cold.
16  You need rest.
17  Don't get upset.
18  You will get well."

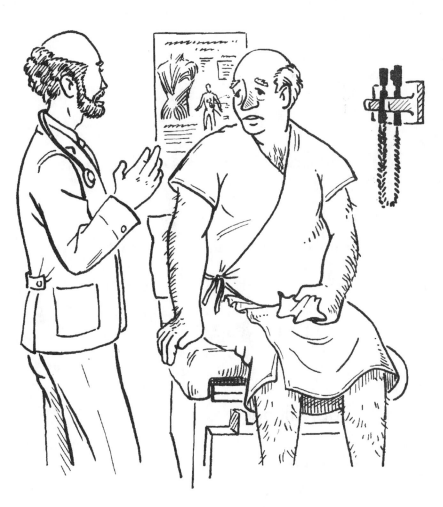

**Circle *yes* or *no*.**

1. Bob is with the doctor.          yes     no

2. Pam feels ill.          yes     no

3. Bob has a bad cold.          yes     no

4. The doctor tells Bob to go to work.          yes     no

5. Bob is a doctor.          yes     no

6. Bob asks the doctor for pills.          yes     no

7. The doctor gives Bob pills.          yes     no

8. Pills can fix a cold.          yes     no

9. Bob needs rest.          yes     no

10. Bob will get well.          yes     no

**Write the word.**

| | |
|---|---|
| what   with | **1.** Bob is _____ the doctor. |
| feed   feel | **2.** Bob doesn't _____ well. |
| cold   call | **3.** He has a bad _____. |
| yells   tells | **4.** The doctor _____ him to rest. |
| think   drink | **5.** He says to _____ a lot of water. |
| desk   asks | **6.** Bob _____ the doctor for pills. |
| Pills   Hills | **7.** _____ can help some things. |
| six   fix | **8.** But pills can't _____ a cold. |
| rest   dust | **9.** Bob needs _____. |
| well   will | **10.** He _____ get well. |

What do you do for a cold?

**Check.**

✔ go to the clinic      ___ drink water

___ stay home from work      ___ drink tea

___ take pills      ___ rest

___ call the doctor      ___ eat soup

___ go to the drugstore      ___ call the boss

**Write.**

I will _go to the clinic._

I will _____

I _____

_____

# THE DOCTOR
# COSTS A LOT

1 Bob is at Hill Street Clinic.
2 He is ready to go home.
3 He stops at the desk.
4 Pam has the bill for Bob.
5 The bill is $75.00.

6   Bob is not happy.

7   The doctor costs a lot.

8   The doctor costs too much.

9   Pam sees that Bob is not happy.

10  Maybe she can help.

11  Pam asks Bob if he has a health plan.

12  Bob does not have a health plan.

13  Pam says, "Some health plans don't cost a lot.

14  May I tell you about a health plan?"

15  Bob says, "Yes. Tell me about it."

16  Bob sits with Pam.

17  She tells him about a plan.

18  Bob will think about it.

19  Maybe he will get a health plan.

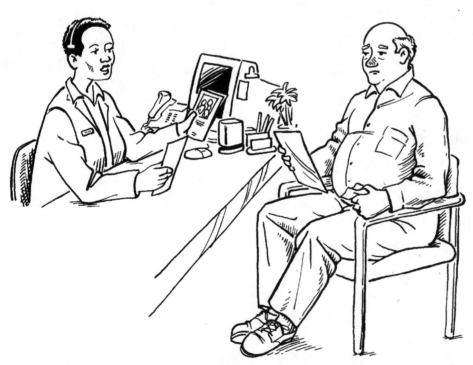

**Circle *yes* or *no*.**

1. Bob is at the shop.       yes      no

2. He is ready to go home.       yes      no

3. The bill is $100.       yes      no

4. Bob is happy.       yes      no

5. The doctor costs a lot.       yes      no

6. The doctor costs a little.       yes      no

7. Bob has a health plan.       yes      no

8. Bob sits with Jack.       yes      no

9. Pam tells Bob about the plan.       yes      no

10. Bob will think about a health plan.       yes      no

**Write the word.**

| | | | |
|---|---|---|---|
| bill | health | not | ready |
| cost | help | plan | too much |

1. Bob is _____ to go home.

2. Pam has the _____ for Bob.

3. Bob is _____ happy.

4. The doctor costs _____.

5. Maybe Pam can _____ Bob.

6. She tells him about the health _____.

7. Some health plans don't _____ a lot.

8. Bob will think about a _____ plan.

32

## Write the word.

| about | at | to |
|---|---|---|

1. Bob is _____ Hill Street Clinic.

2. He is ready _____ go home.

3. He stops _____ the desk.

4. He talks _____ Pam.

5. Pam tells him _____ a plan.

6. Bob will think _____ a health plan.

# GET RID OF STRESS

— ■ —

1 Kim is not well.
2 She is with the doctor at Hill Street Clinic.
3 The doctor thinks Kim has too much stress.

4 Kim says, "I have two jobs. I have two kids.

5 I have a lot of stress.

6 What can I do?"

7 The doctor says, "You can get lots of rest.

8 You can eat good food.

9 Exercise can help.

10 You can jog or walk."

11 Kim says, "I don't have time to rest.

12 And I eat good food.

13 But I can walk to work.

14 I can exercise with the kids."

15 "That will help," says the doctor.

16 "And have some fun. That helps too."

17 Kim says, "I need to win a lot of money.

18 Then I can quit my jobs.

19 That will get rid of my stress!"

**Write the answer.**

1. Why is Kim at Hill Street Clinic?

   _____

2. How many jobs does Kim have?

   _____

3. What does the doctor tell Kim to do?

   _____

   _____

   _____

4. Where can Kim walk?

   _____

5. Who can she exercise with?

   _____

36

## Match. Write.

| doctor | kids | money |
|--------|------|-------|
| exercise | Kim | rest |

1. ___Kim___

2. _____

3. _____

4. _____

5. _____

6. _____

# Circle.

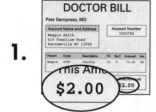

**1.** a lot of money ⟨a little money⟩

**2.** a lot of money a little money

**3.** a lot of money a little money

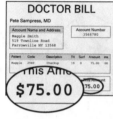

**4.** a lot of money a little money

**5.** a lot of money a little money

## KIM'S PLAN

1 Kim is at home with her kids.
2 Kim says, "I have too much stress.
3 I have to get rid of my stress."

4 Kim tells her kids, "You can help me.
5 You can help me be more healthy."

6 "We eat good food," Kim says.
7 "That helps.
8 But I have to get more rest.
9 And I want to get more exercise."

10 Kim says, "We can exercise together.
11 We can walk in the park.
12 We can exercise at home.
13 We can have fun and be healthy."

14 Kim says, "And we can go to bed early.
15 I can get more rest.
16 Then I will feel a lot better."

**Circle *yes* or *no* about *you*.**

1. You have too much stress.      yes      no

2. You can be more healthy.      yes      no

3. Your kids can help.      yes      no

4. You can eat good food.      yes      no

5. You can exercise at home.      yes      no

6. You can get more rest.      yes      no

7. You can walk to work.      yes      no

8. You can have fun.      yes      no

9. You can walk in the park.      yes      no

10. You can go to bed early.      yes      no

**Ask a partner.**

How do you get rid of stress?
Where do you exercise?
Do you get a lot of rest?

**Write a story.**

**1.** He/She _____ to get rid of stress.

**2.** He/She exercises _____.

**3.** He/She _____ rest.

**Copy the story.**

_____

_____

_____

_____

How can you be more healthy?

**Check.**

\_\_\_\_ get rid of stress      \_\_\_\_ have fun

\_\_\_\_ eat good food      \_\_\_\_ go to bed early

\_\_\_\_ get more rest      \_\_\_\_ walk to work

\_\_\_\_ exercise      \_\_\_\_ play with the kids

\_\_\_\_ walk in the park      \_\_\_\_ take vitamins

**Write.**

I can _____

I can _____

I _____

_____

# ANSWER KEY

## p. 7
1. yes
2. yes
3. no
4. yes
5. yes
6. no
7. yes
8. no
9. no
10. no

## p. 8
1. Hill
2. shops
3. has
4. lives
5. is
6. kids
7. with
8. Street
9. Bob
10. to

## p. 11
1. It is Wednesday.
2. Kim's son has a rash.
3. Kim calls Hill Street Clinic.
4. Her son has to see the doctor.
5. Today, the rash is on his hands and legs.
6. She can bring him to the clinic at 1:00 p.m.

## p. 12
1. Wednesday
2. rash
3. doctor
4. Pam
5. Monday
6. Tuesday
7. hands
8. son

## p. 13
1. is
2. is
3. has
4. has
5. is
6. is

## p. 16
1. yes
2. yes
3. no
4. yes
5. no
6. yes
7. no
8. no
9. yes
10. no

## p. 17
1. bed
2. work
3. boss
4. sick
5. well
6. get
7. clinic
8. thanks
9. call
10. today

## p. 18
1. in
2. in
3. at
4. to
5. to
6. to
7. at
8. to

## p. 21
1. Bob is at Hill Street Clinic.
2. Pam works at Hill Street Clinic.
3. Bob tells Pam he has an appointment with the doctor.
4. Bob spells his last name F-I-N-N.
5. Pam tells Bob to sit.
6. The doctor can see Bob.

## p. 22
1. well
2. works
3. big
4. appointment
5. spell
6. tells
7. sits
8. doctor

# ANSWER KEY

## p. 23
1. no
2. yes
3. no
4. yes
5. no
6. no

## p. 26
1. yes
2. no
3. yes
4. no
5. no
6. yes
7. no
8. no
9. yes
10. yes

## p. 27
1. with
2. feel
3. cold
4. tells
5. drink
6. asks
7. Pills
8. fix
9. rest
10. will

## p. 31
1. no
2. yes
3. no
4. no
5. yes
6. no
7. no
8. no
9. yes
10. yes

## p. 32
1. ready
2. bill
3. not
4. too much
5. help
6. plan
7. cost
8. health

## p. 33
1. at
2. to
3. at
4. to
5. about
6. about

## p. 36
1. Kim is not well.
2. Kim has two jobs.
3. The doctor tells Kim to get lots of rest, eat good food, and exercise.
4. Kim can walk to work.
5. She can exercise with the kids.

## p. 37
1. Kim
2. doctor
3. money
4. exercise
5. rest
6. kids

## p. 38
1. a little money
2. a lot of money
3. a lot of money
4. a little money
5. a little money

# SHORT-VOWEL WORDS

a lot

a lot of

am

an

and

asks

at

bad

bed

Ben

better

big

bill

block

Bob Finn

boss

bring

but

can

can't

chest

clinic

come

cost, costs

desk

doctor

does

drink

exercise

fix

fun

get

get rid of

get well

hands

happy

has, have

has to, have to

have fun

health

health plan

healthy

hello

help, helps

Hill Street

Hill Street Clinic

him

his

if

ill

in

is

it

Jack

job (jobs)

jog

kids

Kim Lee

last

legs

lives

lots

matter

Monday

money

neck

not

of

on

p.m.

Pam

pills

# SHORT-VOWEL WORDS

plan

quit

rash

ready

rest

says

shops

sick

sick of

sit, sits

some

son

spell

stands

stands up

stops

stress

tell, tells

thank you

that

then

things

think, thinks

this

together

too much

up

upset

want, wants

want to, wants to

was

water

Wednesday

welcome

well

what

what's

will

win

with

yes

# OTHER WORDS

a

about

appointment

be

call, calls

cold

do

don't

early

eat

feel

first

food

for

go

good

he

her

home

I

maybe

me

more

my

name

need

need to, needs to

OK

or

park

see, sees

she

the

time

to

today

too

Tuesday

two

walk

we

work, works

you

your